Wake

GW00870440

The turtle
in the pond
told...

3

the beaver
in the dam.

4

5

The beaver
in the dam
told...

the frog
on the log.

The frog
on the log
told...

the squirrel
in the tree.

12

The squirrel in the tree told...

15

the snake
in the burrow.

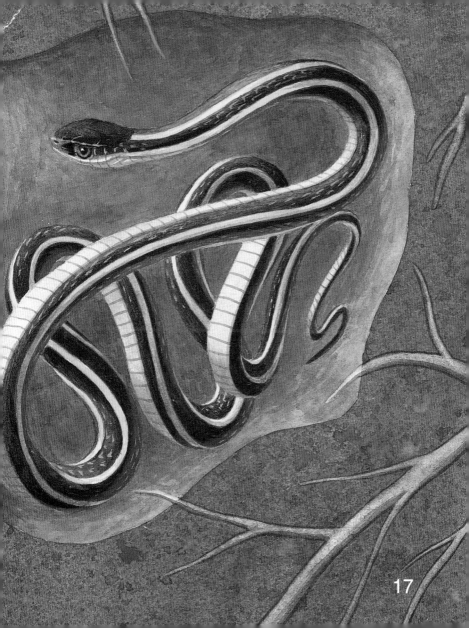

17

The snake
in the burrow
told...

the bear
in the den.

21

Wake up!
Wake up!

Spring is here.